SCHOOL KIDS BEST
ACTIVITY BIBLE

scandinavia

School Kids Best Activity Bible

1st edition, 5th print
Copyright © Scandinavia Publishing House 2023
Scandinavia Publishing House
www.sph.as | info@sph.as
Illustrator: Fabiano Fiorin
Text: Andrew Newton
Activities, Layout & cover design: Collaborate Agency
Activity editor: Linda Vium

Printed in China
ISBN 9788772031651

Contents

God Makes Everything
Genesis 1–3

In the very beginning, God made the world, and it was all very good. He made the earth and the sea, the sun and the stars, the plants and the animals, and last of all He made the first man and the first woman. Their names were Adam and Eve, and they lived together in a beautiful garden with God. God had only one rule for Adam and Eve, and that was to never eat the fruit from the tree of the knowledge of good and evil.

He warned them that if they ate from that tree, they would die. One day, a snake tricked Eve into eating some of the fruit, and she gave some to Adam and he ate it too. They were ashamed because they had sinned and disobeyed God. Now they could no longer live in the garden with God, because He is holy and sinful people cannot be near Him.

Find and Count

How many of each item can you find? Write your answers in the boxes.

Pink Flowers ☐   Flying Birds ☐   Butterflies ☐   Horses ☐

Draw and Color

Design your own Garden of Eden.

Crossword

Fill in the blanks. Use the story text to help you.

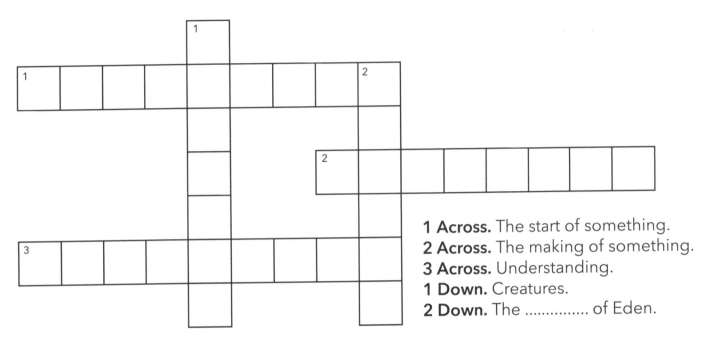

1 Across. The start of something.
2 Across. The making of something.
3 Across. Understanding.
1 Down. Creatures.
2 Down. The .... of Eden.

Spot the Odd One

Spot the odd one out in each row of pictures.

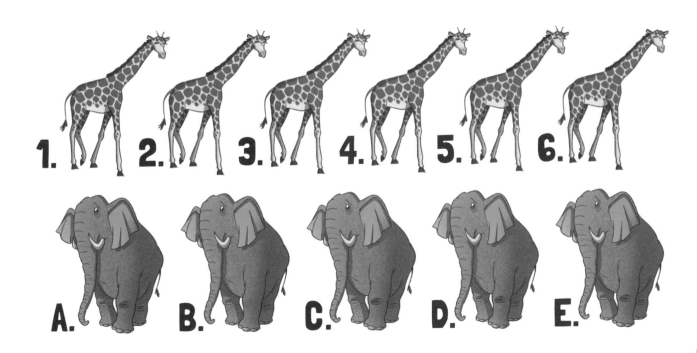

Descriptions

What part of God's universe is being described?

....

is the place that is made of water, where all the fish and sea creatures live.

....

is the place where the sun, moon, stars, and clouds are, and the birds fly.

....

is the place where Adam and Eve walked, where the trees and flowers grow.

Color the Bible Verse

I praise you because I am fearfully and wonderfully made.

Psalm 139:14

Dot to Dot

Connect the dots to see what is hiding in the Garden of Eden.

Noah Builds a Boat

Genesis 6–8

Because of sin, the world got worse and worse. One day, God saw that there was only one man who still loved Him, and his name was Noah. God told Noah to build an ark—a big boat—because He was going to flood the world and destroy all the evil people. He sent two of every kind of animal to Noah to keep them safe from the flood.

Noah did what God told him. When Noah's family and the animals were all in the ark, God sent the flood. It rained and rained until the tallest mountains were covered. Noah and his family and the animals stayed in the ark until all the water had dried up again.

When Noah came out of the ark, he thanked God for protecting his family. God put a rainbow in the sky as a promise that He would never flood the whole earth again.

Sticker Game

Find the sticker shapes on page 114 to complete the picture.

Do not be afraid, for I am with you.

Isaiah 43:5

Maze

Find the route that takes you to the ark.

START

FINISH

12

Spot the Differences

Can you spot 8 differences between the 2 pictures?

Descriptions

What animals are being described?

....

has a very long neck, and is covered in a patchy pattern.

....

is a large type of bear with black and white spots, and it eats shoots and leaves.

....

is a heavy gray animal with a trunk, tusks, and large floppy ears.

Word Scramble

Unscramble the animal names.

FRAGIFE

NADAP

LEPANTHE

DOCROLICE

Draw and Color

Color the rainbow and draw some animals underneath it.

Abraham and Sarah Trust God
Genesis 12:1–9; 21:1–7

There was a man named Abraham who loved God. He and his wife Sarah were both old, and they didn't have any children. God made a promise to Abraham that he would have as many descendants as there are stars in the sky, and all the people in the world would be blessed through him.

Abraham didn't know how God would do what He promised, but he believed that He could and that He would. One day, God told Abraham that in one year, Sarah would have a baby boy. Abraham and Sarah laughed because it seemed impossible, but God can do anything. A year later, their son was born.

They named him Isaac, which means "laughter," and they were filled with joy. God had kept His promise to give them a son, and He would keep His other promises as well.

Word Match

Match the words that mean the same thing.

PROMISE	HAPPINESS
BELIEVE	AMUSEMENT
LAUGHTER	VOW
JOY	TRUST

Sequences

Which image is missing from each sequence? Write the correct letter in the box.

1.

2.

A.  **B.**  **C.**  **D.**

Shape Puzzle

Complete the scene with the shape stickers on page 115.

Dot to Dot

Who is playing in the desert?

Key Coded Coloring

Use the color key to color the picture.

▲ = purple   ● = yellow   ▼ = black   ■ = brown

◆ = red   ⬡ = blue   ● = orange

Family Tree

Each description is about someone from Abraham's family. Read each one carefully and write down the name of the person being described.

Abraham   Sarah

Isaac

....

was the wife of Abraham and mother of Isaac.

....

was the son whose name means "laughter."

....

would have as many descendants as there are stars in the sky.

Word Search

Find the words in the grid.

B	T	B	L	E	J	X	C	U	A	J	R	P	S	F	T	A
A	F	V	E	Q	H	O	W	I	S	B	U	Q	D	O	N	U
U	D	L	M	U	K	R	Z	S	N	N	R	L	K	S	M	B
D	W	H	A	O	T	V	E	A	Y	F	P	A	I	A	Q	C
W	F	Z	R	U	E	R	Q	A	V	A	N	M	H	B	J	R
P	N	P	Q	H	G	K	O	C	Y	U	B	C	P	A	N	X
O	E	X	B	P	A	H	C	Y	K	T	D	T	G	L	M	V
I	S	A	R	A	H	J	T	R	V	X	Q	G	I	H	H	O
U	L	T	W	I	F	D	R	E	Y	J	Q	S	O	A	V	T
P	H	C	U	E	L	X	Z	M	R	F	E	L	W	M	R	Z

Abraham
Sarah
Isaac
Laughter

Joseph Saves His Family

Genesis 37; 39-45

Joseph had eleven brothers, but his father loved him the most. His brothers were jealous of Joseph, so they sold him as a slave in Egypt. God was watching over Joseph, though. One day the king of Egypt had a dream, and no one could tell him what it meant. One of the king's servants knew that God told Joseph the meanings of dreams, so the king told Joseph his dream.

Joseph told the king that his dream meant there would be seven years of plenty, followed by seven years of famine. The king put Joseph in charge of saving up food to prepare for the famine, making him the second most powerful person in Egypt.

When Joseph's family came to Egypt to buy food, he forgave them. "You meant to hurt me," he said, "but God used it for good, to save all your lives and many more."

Code Breaker

Fill in the Bible verse using the secret code.

A=1
B=2
C=3
D=4
E=5
F=6
G=7
H=8
I=9
J=10
K=11
L=12
M=13
N=14
O=15
P=16
Q=17
R=18
S=19
T=20
U=21
V=22
W=23
X=24
Y=25
Z=26

9 ○

8 5 18 5 2 25 ○ ○ ○ ○ ○ ○

16 21 20 ○ ○ ○   **25 15 21** ○ ○ ○   **9 14** ○ ○

3 8 1 18 7 5 ○ ○ ○ ○ ○ ○   **15 6** ○ ○

20 8 5 ○ ○ ○   **23 8 15 12 5** ○ ○ ○ ○ ○

12 1 14 4 ○ ○ ○ ○   **15 6** ○ ○

5 7 25 16 20 ○ ○ ○ ○ ○ .

Genesis 41:41

Crossword

Use the story text to help you.

1 Across. Wanting what somebody else has.

2 Across. A vision that comes in sleep.

1 Down. One more than ten.

2 Down. A shortage of food.

3 Down. A person in the service of another.

Story Quiz

Answer the questions about the story.

1. How many brothers did Joseph have?

....

2. Where was Joseph sold as a slave?

....

3. How many years of plenty were there?

....

4. Who had the dream that predicted the famine?

....

Draw and Color

Design a coat for Joseph.

Find and Count

How many of each item can you find?

Palm Trees ☐ Sheep ☐ Walking Sticks ☐ Sandals ☐

For I know the plans I have for you.

Jeremiah 29:11

Line Maze

Which line leads Joseph to his coat?

A
B
C

Moses Leads God's People to Freedom

Exodus 1–14

The king of Egypt was afraid of the Israelites, so he made them slaves and ordered that all their baby boys should be thrown in the Nile River. Moses' mother saved him by putting him in a floating basket. The princess found him and raised him as her son.

When Moses was grown up, God appeared to him in a burning bush and told him to go tell the king to let His people, the Israelites, go free. Moses did what God said, but the king refused to let God's people go. God sent ten plagues on Egypt until the king finally let the Israelites go.

After they left, the king changed his mind and chased after them with an army, but God parted the sea so His people could escape. The king and his army tried to follow them, but God made the water go back over the king's army. His people were safe!

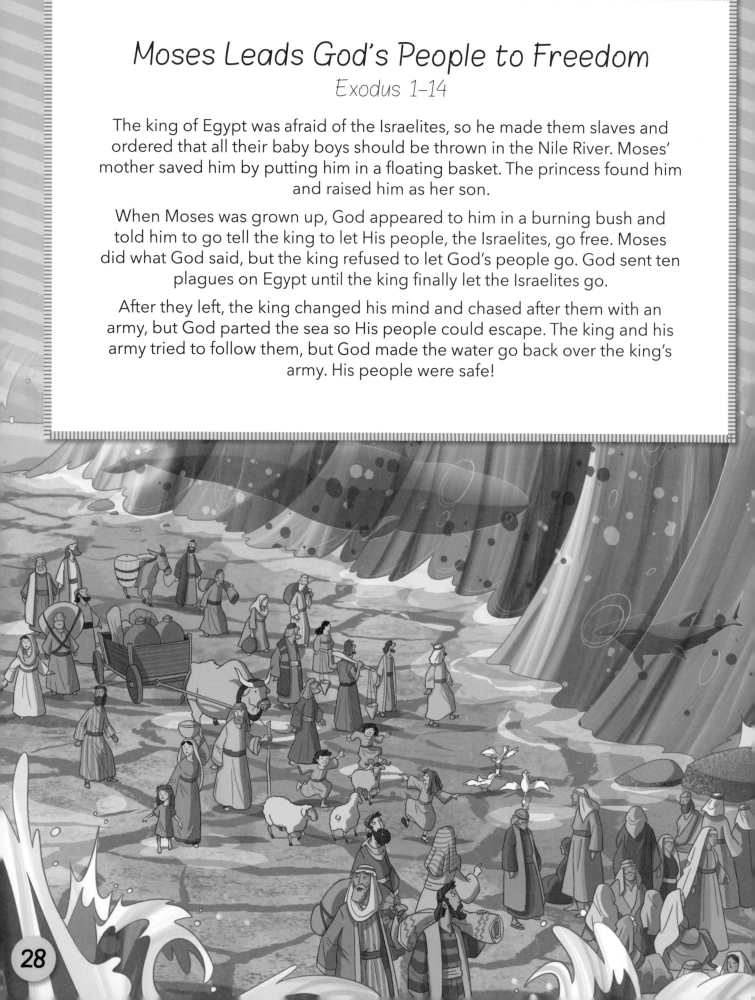

Picture Sudoku

Fill in the sudoku. Which images go where?

A.  **B.**  **C.**  **D.**

Maze

Follow the path through the sea.

START

FINISH

Color the Bible Verse

Trust in the Lord with all your heart.

Proverbs 3:5

Puzzle

Where do the scrambled puzzle shapes go?

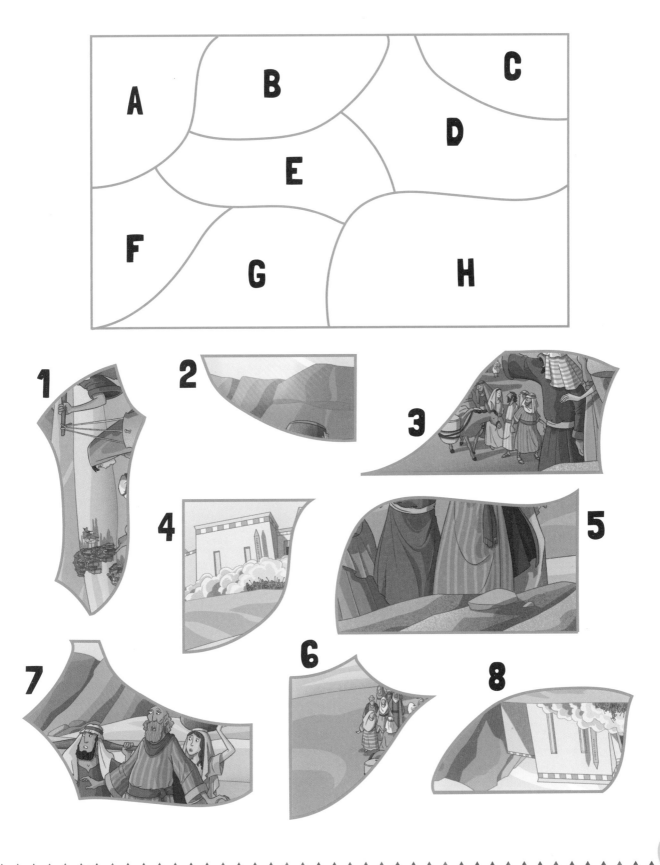

Spot the Differences

Can you spot the 8 differences between these 2 pictures?

Spot the Odd One

Spot the odd one out in each row of pictures.

1.   2.   3   4   5

A.   B.   C.   D.   E.

Word Scramble

Unscramble the words from the story.

ELAIRSTIES   GAULPE

TYPEG   SEMOS

Ruth Stays with Naomi
The Book of Ruth

Naomi was living in the land of Moab with her husband and two sons. Unfortunately, Naomi's husband and sons died, leaving her and her daughters-in-law alone. Naomi decided to go back to Israel, and she told her daughters-in-law to find new husbands in Moab.

Her daughter-in-law Ruth refused. She said, "Where you go, I'll go, and where you stay, I'll stay." Ruth and Naomi came to Naomi's hometown of Bethlehem at harvest time, so Ruth went out in the fields to gather grain for them to eat.

The owner of the field Ruth went to was a relative of Naomi named Boaz. Boaz wanted to take care of Ruth and Naomi, so he gave Ruth as much grain as she could carry and told her to come back the next day. Later Boaz and Ruth got married and had a son. Naomi lived with them, happy to have a new family.

Spot the Differences

Can you spot the 8 differences between these 2 pictures?

Code Breaker

Fill in the Bible verse using the secret code (on page 23).

25 15 21 18   **16 5 15 16 12 5**   **23 9 12 12**

◯◯◯◯ ◯◯◯◯◯◯ ◯◯◯◯

2 5   **13 25**   **16 5 15 16 12 5**   **1 14 4**

◯◯ ◯◯ ◯◯◯◯◯◯ ◯◯◯

25 15 21 18   **7 15 4**   **13 25**   **7 15 4**

◯◯◯◯ ◯◯◯ ◯◯ ◯◯◯.

Ruth 1:16

Family Tree

Each description is about someone from Ruth's family. Read each one carefully and write down the name of the person being described.

Naomi

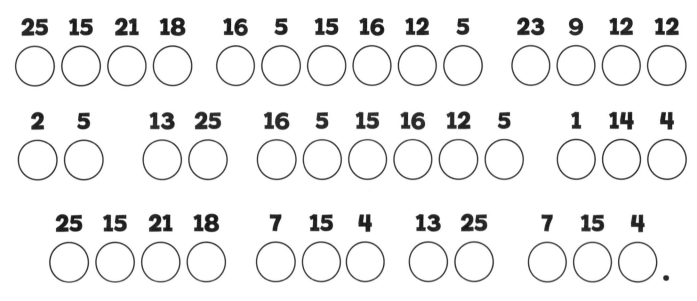

....

was related to Naomi and married Ruth.

Boaz   *Ruth*

....

was Ruth's mother-in-law. She returned to Bethlehem when her husband and sons died.

Obed

....

was Naomi's daughter-in-law and the wife of Boaz, whom she had a son with.

Key Coded Coloring

Use the color key to color the picture.

▲ = red ● = orange ▼ = green ■ = brown ◆ = skin color ⬡ = yellow

Find the Shadow

Which shadow matches the picture?

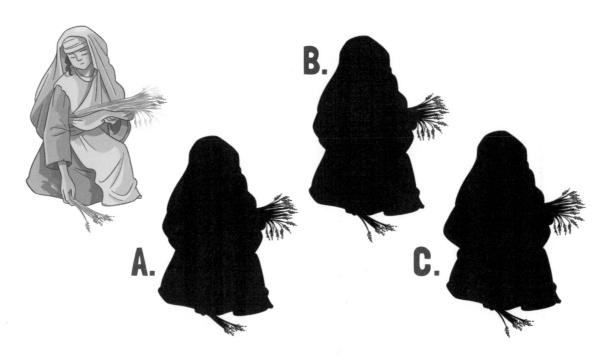

Color the Bible Verse

Ask and it will be given to you; seek and you will find.

Matthew 7:7

Shape Puzzle

Complete the scene with the shape stickers on page 115.

Esther Saves Her People
The Book of Esther

Esther and her cousin Mordecai lived in the land of Persia, but they were Jews, God's chosen people. Xerxes, the king of Persia, held a beauty contest to choose his new queen. He chose Esther out of all the young women in the kingdom to be his queen, but he didn't know she was a Jew.

Haman, one of Xerxes' advisors, hated Mordecai, so he asked the king to make a law ordering the death of all Jews. When Esther heard about this law, she went before the king, even though she was uninvited. She asked him to bring Haman to a dinner with her. When she was alone with Xerxes and Haman, Esther told the king all about Haman's plan to destroy her people. Xerxes was so angry that he had Haman executed the same way Haman had wanted to execute Mordecai. Then Mordecai and Esther made a new law that protected their people.

Word Search

Find the words in the grid.

N	R	Q	N	Z	M	K	B	W	R	W	E	P	J	A	Q	D
U	Z	E	M	G	A	I	N	D	Z	S	V	C	O	Z	V	O
Q	T	K	U	O	Y	N	J	U	J	E	S	T	H	E	R	H
H	X	V	C	E	R	A	O	X	G	M	X	Y	D	L	T	P
F	P	Y	V	S	A	D	Q	F	H	I	K	P	X	U	B	H
S	K	I	A	O	T	L	E	R	A	J	B	G	E	A	B	M
O	P	E	R	S	I	A	F	C	M	C	U	T	R	S	E	K
X	W	I	X	D	O	T	C	U	A	X	M	F	X	H	C	I
L	J	S	B	D	W	P	G	X	N	I	Z	K	E	C	N	R
H	E	Q	I	Y	L	V	M	F	G	R	W	Y	S	L	E	A

Mordecai

Esther

Xerxes

Persia

Haman

Word Scramble

Unscramble the words from the story.

CODEMIRA

SREXEX

ASPIRE

TEHSRE

Word Match

Match the words that mean the same thing.

COUSIN	PREFERRED
LAND	EMPIRE
CHOSEN	ALLURE
BEAUTY	COMPANION
KING	REGION
WOMAN	RULER
KINGDOM	KILL
ADVISOR	RELATIVE
FRIEND	GUIDE
EXECUTE	FEMALE

Sequences

Which image is missing from each sequence?

1.

2.

Crossword

Use the story text to help you.

1 **Across.** A relative.
2 **Across.** Not welcomed.
1 **Down.** The main meal of the day.
2 **Down.** Physical attractiveness.

Don't worry about anything; instead, pray about everything.

Philippians 4:6 (NLT)

Sticker Game

Find the sticker shapes on page 114 to complete the picture.

God Protects Daniel

Daniel 6

Daniel lived in Babylon because God's people had been captured by the Babylonian kings. He loved God and was one of King Darius's most trusted advisors. The other advisors were jealous of Daniel, so they came up with a plan to get rid of him.

They went to Darius and said, "You should make a new law that everyone in the whole kingdom must pray to you and only to you. If anyone doesn't, that person must be thrown into the den of lions." Darius passed the law, but Daniel kept praying to God three times a day. The advisors told Darius that Daniel had broken the new law, and Darius was very sad. He had no choice but to throw Daniel into the lions' den.

The next day, Darius came to see if, somehow, Daniel was still alive. He was! God had protected Daniel and sent an angel to shut the lions' mouths.

Find and Count

How many lions can you count in the den?

Maze

Follow the path out of the lions' den.

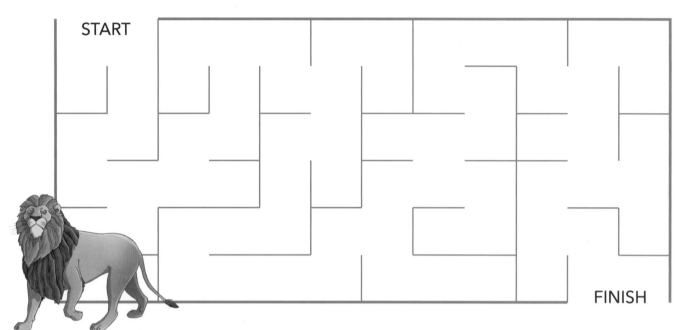

START

FINISH

Story Quiz

Answer the questions about the story.

1. Where did Daniel live?

....

2. How many times a day did Daniel pray?

....

3. What was the king's name?

....

4. What was the new law?

....

Puzzle

Where do the scrambled puzzle shapes go?

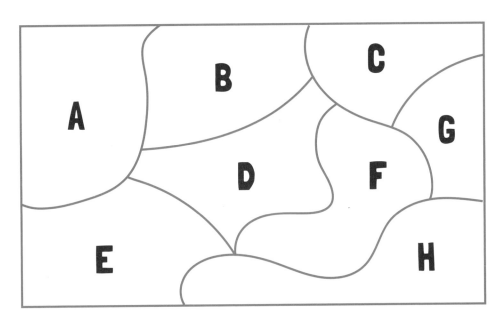

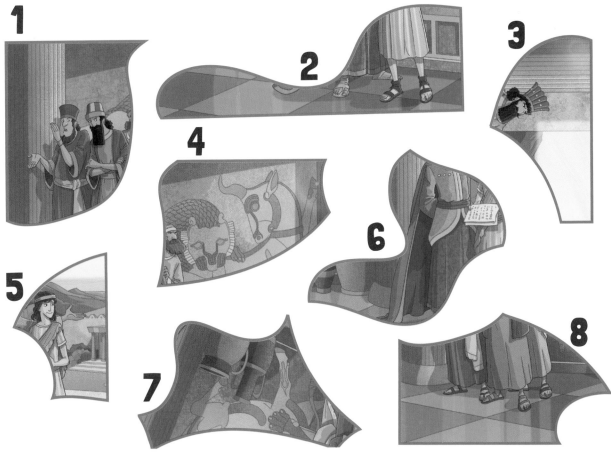

Descriptions

What elements from the story are being described? Fill in the blanks.

....

are big cats, with sharp teeth and claws! The males have long manes.

....

is the place where Daniel was thrown for breaking the law.

....

is the being who was sent from God to shut the lions' mouths.

Word Scramble

Unscramble the words from the story.

....
LABOBYN

....
RIADSU

....
ELANDI

....
GRAPYIN

Picture Sudoku

Fill in the sudoku. Which images go where?

A.  **B.**  **C.**  **D.**

A Whale Swallows Jonah
The Book of Jonah

God told Jonah to go preach to the city of Nineveh and tell them to turn from their evil ways. Jonah hated Nineveh and wanted them to be destroyed for their sin, so he ran away and got on a boat going as far from Nineveh as possible.

That night, a storm was almost sinking the boat, and Jonah told the sailors that it was his fault, since he was running away from God. "You have to throw me overboard," he said. "Then the storm will stop." The sailors did what Jonah said, and as soon as he hit the water, the storm stopped.

God sent a big whale to swallow Jonah, and he was stuck in the whale's belly for three days. On the third day, the whale spit Jonah out on the shore, and this time he went straight to Nineveh. The Ninevites listened to Jonah's message and turned to God.

Line Maze

Which line takes Jonah to the whale?

Find the Shadow

Which shadow matches the picture?

A.

B.

C.

D.

Spot the Differences

Can you spot the 8 differences between the 2 pictures?

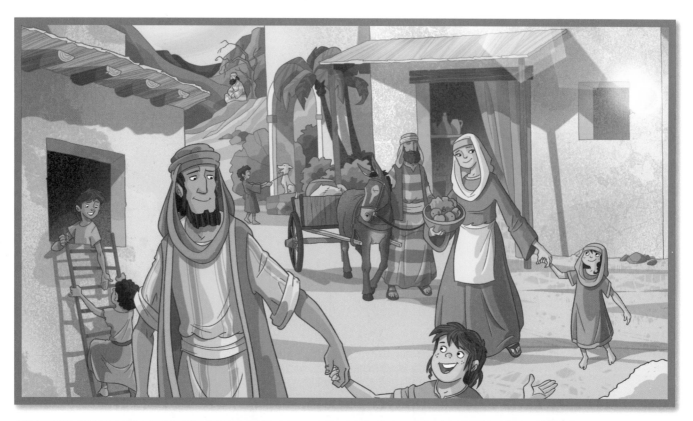

Crossword

Use the story text to help you.

1 Across. A type of bird that is also a word for gulp.

2 Across. A communicated piece of information.

3 Across. A person who sails.

1 Down. Going down.

2 Down. A very large animal that lives in the sea.

Word Search

Find the words in the grid.

D	N	H	E	Y	R	A	K	P	B	V	U	C	N	V	T	Q
C	J	N	O	I	N	B	G	V	E	R	O	B	I	A	E	K
H	W	P	T	V	J	W	D	W	H	A	L	E	N	Z	X	W
E	Q	R	G	C	E	A	X	Y	U	M	E	Q	E	A	F	M
E	C	E	D	V	P	R	A	L	E	S	J	T	V	P	C	H
S	I	A	H	F	A	K	B	W	K	Z	N	D	I	D	C	G
M	X	C	P	O	R	B	J	O	P	E	P	R	T	W	G	H
B	L	H	Z	Q	I	Z	M	K	A	O	L	N	E	U	Y	R
V	J	O	N	A	H	B	F	X	W	R	C	U	S	P	L	J
T	S	E	S	Y	O	F	M	J	V	X	D	M	W	I	O	Z

Jonah

Ninevites

Overboard

Whale

Preach

55

Story Quiz

Answer the questions about the story.

1. Where did God tell Jonah to go?

....

2. Did Jonah like Nineveh?

....

3. Why did God send a storm?

....

4. What did the sailors do to stop the storm?

....

5. What happened when Jonah hit the water?

....

6. How long was Jonah stuck in the whale's belly?

....

7. How did Jonah escape the whale?

....

8. What happened when Jonah went to Nineveh?

....

The LORD is good to all; he has compassion on all he has made.

Psalm 145:9

The King Is Born
Matthew 2:1–12; Luke 2:1–20

Mary and her husband, Joseph, were traveling to Bethlehem, and she was very pregnant. This was not just any pregnancy, however. The baby she was carrying was Jesus, the Son of God. There was no room for them to stay in the inn, but the innkeeper had a stable where they could sleep.

While they were there, Mary gave birth to baby Jesus. Mary and Joseph were filled with joy to meet their baby, who was God's own Son. Angels told nearby shepherds that the Savior of the world had been born, and they came to see Him right away. A bright star shone down on the stable where Jesus was.

Far away, some wise men saw the star, and they traveled until they found Jesus. "We have come to worship the King of the Jews," they said, and they gave Him gifts of gold and rare spices.

Dot to Dot

Who is in the stable?

Spot the Odd One

Spot the odd one out in each row of pictures.

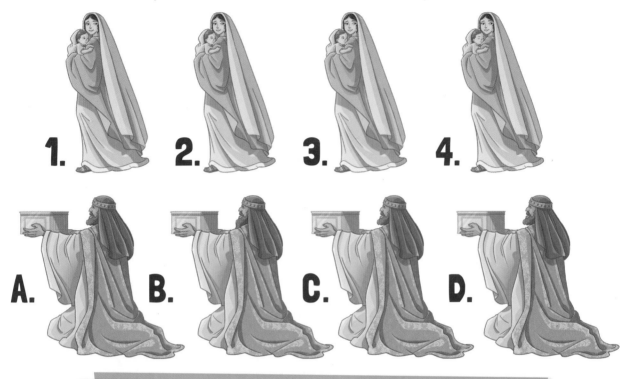

Line Maze

Which line leads the wise man to his camel?

Sticker Game

Find the sticker shapes on page 114 to complete the picture.

Maze

Follow the path to the manger.

START

FINISH

Match the gifts to their descriptions.

1. Gold

A. This gift is in a pot with a round lid. It is a rare spice that was reserved for the worship of God. This gift represents the fact that Jesus was indeed divine.

2. Frankincense

B. This gift is in a pot with a pointed lid. It is a rare spice that was used for burials. It is said to represent that Jesus came into the world to die for our sins.

3. Myrrh

C. This gift is in a rectangular box. It represents the fact that Jesus was royal and would rule the Kingdom of God.

....

Word Scramble

Unscramble the words from the story.

....

ENINPREKE   **HEDPRESH**

....

SWIPROH   **ROVSAI**

Jesus Feeds a Huge Crowd
John 6:1–15

One day, a huge crowd of people had come to hear Jesus teach them about God's Kingdom. There was no town nearby, and it was getting late, so they needed food. "You give them some food," Jesus told His disciples. The disciples looked around, but all they could find was a young boy with a packed lunch of two small fish and five small loaves of bread. Jesus told them to have everyone sit down.

There were more than five thousand people in the crowd, but Jesus thanked God for the food and started breaking it into pieces. He gave the pieces to the disciples to hand out to the crowd.

By the time they were done, everyone had enough to eat and was satisfied. They even had enough leftovers to fill twelve baskets! Everyone was amazed at the miracle Jesus had performed, and they said, "He must be the Prophet of God!"

Spot the Differences

Can you spot the 8 differences between the 2 pictures?

Find and Count

How many of each item can you find?

Baskets ☐

Loaves of bread ☐

Fish ☐

Color the Bible Verse

Give thanks to the LORD, for he is good.

Psalm 107:1

Line Maze

Which line leads to the basket of fish?

A B C

67

Word Match

Match the words that mean the same thing.

HUNGRY	CONTENT
SATISFIED	ASTOUNDED
MIRACLE	RAVENOUS
AMAZED	PHENOMENON

Word Scramble

Unscramble the words from the story.

PLECSIDSI

IFHS

VOLASE

VRESLOTEF

Key Coded Coloring

Use the color key to color the picture.

▲ = blue   ● = brown   ▼ = yellow   ■ = red   ◆ = green   ⬡ = skin color

Jesus Loves the Little Children
Matthew 19:13–14

There were some parents who wanted to bring their children to see Jesus, but His disciples turned them away. "Jesus is too busy to be bothered with children," they said.

But Jesus corrected them. "Let the little children come to me," He said. "The Kingdom of God belongs to children and people like them. In fact, if anyone comes to me and doesn't have faith like a small child, that person will not see the Kingdom of Heaven."

Jesus loves all people, young and old, big and small. He wants everyone to come to Him.

Code Breaker

Fill in the Bible verse using the secret code (on page 23).

23 8 15 5 22 5 18   **23 5 12 3 15 13 5 19**

◯◯◯◯◯◯◯ ◯◯◯◯◯◯◯◯

20 8 9 19   **12 9 20 20 12 5**

◯◯◯◯ ◯◯◯◯◯◯

3 8 9 12 4   **9 14 13 25**   **14 1 13 5**

◯◯◯◯◯ ◯◯◯◯ ◯◯◯◯

23 5 12 3 15 13 5 19   **13 5**

◯◯◯◯◯◯◯◯ ◯◯.

Luke 9:48

Find the Shadow

Which shadows are the odd ones out?

Crossword

Use the story text to help you.

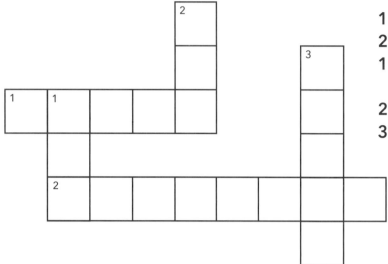

1 Across. Youthful, not very old.
2 Across. A follower of Jesus.
1 Down. Having been alive for a long time.
2 Down. Large.
3 Down. Little.

Word Search

Find the words in the grid.

D	Q	O	G	Z	S	E	T	Y	K	E	V	E	H	B	P	N
T	J	D	I	S	C	I	P	L	E	S	W	O	R	D	B	F
L	B	S	K	X	H	M	N	V	K	Z	H	L	A	H	J	K
W	N	F	A	Q	I	G	E	P	Q	I	H	M	I	C	U	T
C	O	I	Y	D	L	M	U	A	W	R	N	V	G	Q	Y	A
R	H	B	H	V	D	O	F	R	C	L	O	G	B	P	I	O
F	U	M	R	N	R	T	I	E	F	E	N	I	D	S	X	F
X	H	E	A	V	E	N	X	N	S	P	U	J	A	O	W	L
P	Q	L	O	D	N	M	Q	T	K	S	A	I	M	D	M	X
J	V	Z	B	S	P	Z	G	S	X	H	I	Q	C	Y	E	I

Parents
Disciples
Children
Kingdom
Heaven

Shape Puzzle

Complete the scene with the shape stickers on page 115.

Picture Sudoku

Fill in the sudoku. Which images go where?

A.  **B.**  **C.**  **D.**

Let the little children come to me, and do not hinder them, for the Kingdom of God belongs to such as these.

Luke 18:16 (NLT)

Zacchaeus Climbs a Tree

Luke 19:1–10

Zacchaeus was a very short man. He collected taxes for the government, and he often took more from people than he was supposed to and kept the extra for himself. When he heard that Jesus was in town, he wanted to see Him. Since he was so short, Zacchaeus had to climb a tree to see over the crowd. When Jesus saw Zacchaeus up in the tree, He said, "Zacchaeus, come down from there. I want to come to your house today."

Zacchaeus was so excited! Jesus was coming to his house! He ran home and got a big feast ready for Jesus and His disciples. At the dinner, Zacchaeus said, "Teacher, I am going to give half of my belongings to the poor, and if I have cheated anyone, I will pay that person back four times as much!" Because Jesus showed His love to Zacchaeus, Zacchaeus wanted to show love to others, too.

Maze

Guide Zacchaeus to Jesus.

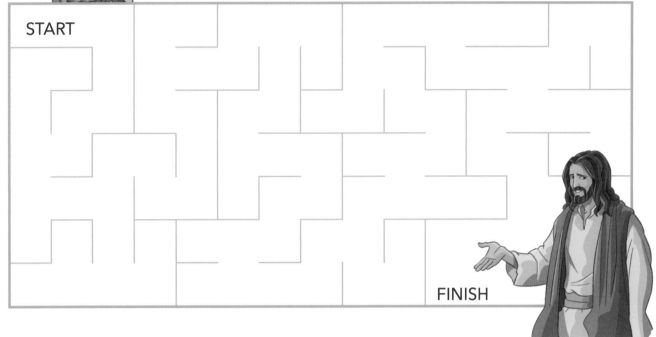

START

FINISH

Color the Bible Verse

He has removed our sins as far from us as the east is from the west.

Psalm 103:12 (NLT)

Spot the Differences

Can you spot the 8 differences between these 2 pictures?

Puzzle

Where do the scrambled puzzle shapes go?

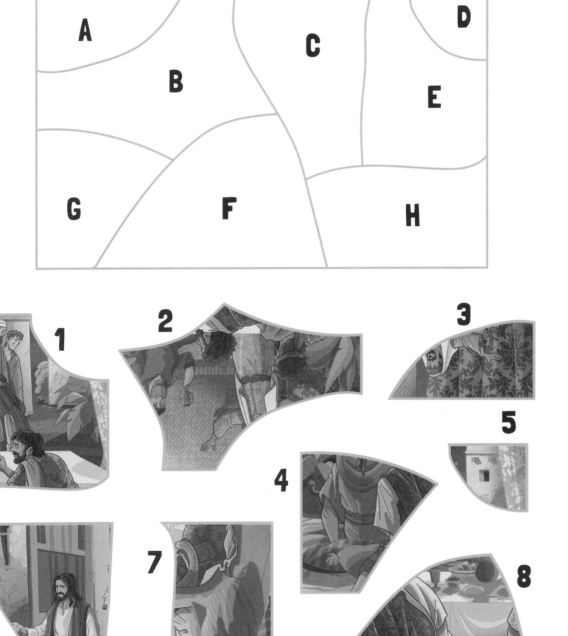

Dot to Dot

What is the Roman guard holding?

Crossword

Use the story text to help you.

1 Across. Acted unfairly.
2 Across. In addition to.
3 Across. A large plant with a trunk, branches, roots, and leaves.
1 Down. Someone who teaches.
2 Down. Money that citizens must pay to their government.

Sequences

Which image is missing from each sequence?

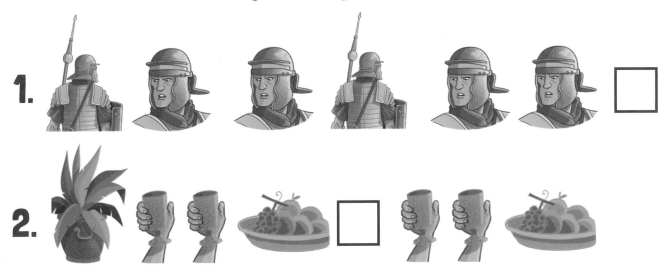

1.

2.

 A.  B.  C.   D.  E.

Jesus Dies for Our Sins

Matthew 27:11-66

The leaders of the Israelites didn't like Jesus. He threatened their power by teaching people how to worship God in their hearts instead of following the rules the leaders had made. The leaders put Jesus on trial and decided to kill Him by putting Him on a cross. This was the most painful way for someone to die, and Jesus let them kill Him this way, even though He was perfect and had never sinned or done anything wrong.

Jesus suffered as much as it is possible for someone to suffer, and then He died. Jesus was God's Son, so He didn't have to die. Death is the price of sin, but Jesus never sinned. He chose to die in our place to pay the price for all our sins. Because Jesus took our place, God can forgive us for our sins and wash them away. If we believe that Jesus died for us, He forgives us and makes us clean.

Spot the Differences

Can you spot the 8 differences between these 2 pictures?

Word Match

Match the words that mean the same thing.

LEADER INTIMIDATE

THREATEN LAWS

RULES RULER

SUFFER ENDURE

Word Scramble

Unscramble the words from the story.

TREPFEC   LRITA

NIULFAP   SEJUS

Story Quiz

Answer the questions about the story.

1. Why didn't the Israelite leaders like Jesus?

....

2. Why was Jesus perfect?

....

3. Why does God forgive us for our sins?

....

4. How was Jesus killed?

....

Word Search

Find the words in the grid.

J	W	F	L	Q	D	M	X	B	O	S	S	I	M	C	V	J
R	A	N	W	E	J	V	K	Q	M	E	I	P	N	W	H	A
D	P	O	T	T	N	C	V	R	H	Y	X	N	U	G	J	F
H	V	G	H	L	Y	S	H	P	W	N	V	I	F	R	P	D
U	F	O	R	G	I	V	E	N	E	S	S	O	H	U	T	G
I	T	J	E	B	U	G	Y	O	V	R	U	T	K	Q	L	T
B	M	I	A	L	K	C	R	U	C	I	F	I	X	I	O	N
K	P	N	T	H	N	A	W	J	U	M	F	E	W	M	I	P
R	F	X	E	W	L	G	D	H	B	N	E	P	C	S	A	C
C	Q	M	N	S	E	P	V	F	J	L	R	K	Y	T	X	E

Forgiveness

Crucifixion

Suffer

Threaten

Sinful

Perfect

85

Counting

How many crosses can you count?

Sticker Game

Find the sticker shapes on page 114 to complete the picture.

Jesus Rises Again
Matthew 28; Luke 24:1-12

Because Jesus is God's perfect Son, He didn't stay dead. After He died, His disciples buried Him in a tomb. Three days later, Mary and Mary Magdalene, two women who had followed Jesus, went to put some perfume on His body to keep it from smelling bad.

When they got to the tomb, the stone that blocked the entrance had been rolled away, and there were two angels sitting on it. The angels said, "Why are you looking for someone alive among the dead? Jesus isn't here; He has risen!"

The women ran back and told the disciples what the angels had said, and later Jesus even appeared to them in the house where they were staying. He let them touch Him, and He ate with them. It was true! He was alive again! Jesus defeated death, and now anyone who believes in Him will also rise again to live with Him forever!

Crossword

Use the story text to help you.

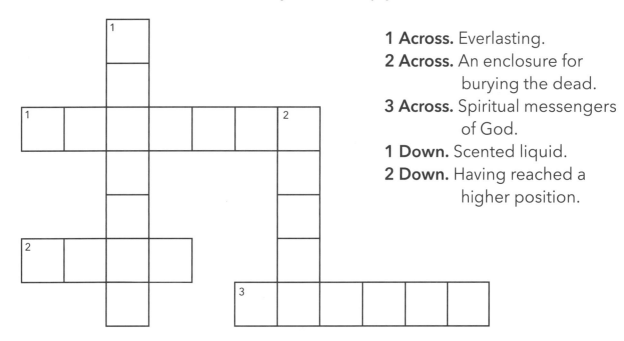

1 Across. Everlasting.
2 Across. An enclosure for burying the dead.
3 Across. Spiritual messengers of God.
1 Down. Scented liquid.
2 Down. Having reached a higher position.

Find the Shadow

Which shadow is the odd one out?

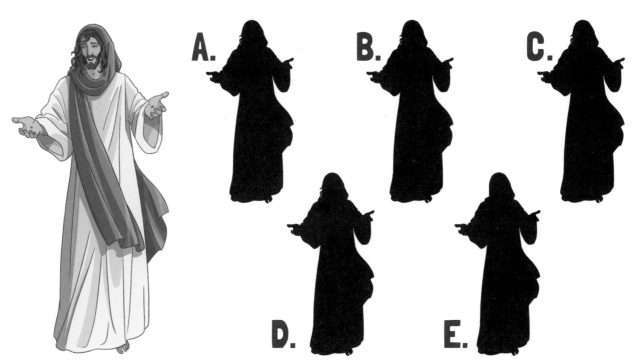

A. B. C. D. E.

Shape Puzzle

Complete the scene with the shape stickers on page 115.

I am the resurrection and the life. Anyone who believes in me will live, even after dying.

John 11:25 (NLT)

Word Search

Find the words in the grid.

C	I	P	J	E	N	C	O	L	N	M	G	I	O	K	N	A
M	O	K	N	L	A	O	P	D	I	S	C	I	P	L	E	S
K	A	I	R	G	K	F	L	B	I	J	D	L	I	Q	L	H
F	W	G	Z	I	R	L	Q	I	H	R	N	P	M	J	A	J
O	O	G	D	P	E	R	F	U	M	E	N	A	K	L	N	I
B	M	D	G	A	I	O	K	J	P	N	L	N	I	E	Q	O
P	E	O	I	D	L	K	I	Q	D	A	K	G	F	P	B	M
H	N	M	L	J	K	E	L	O	N	G	P	E	J	L	M	C
K	E	J	I	M	B	R	N	R	I	O	R	L	P	C	K	R
A	P	L	F	J	I	H	Q	E	S	J	M	S	J	N	P	E

Angels
Magdalene
Perfume
Women
Disciples

Code Breaker

Fill in the Bible verse using the secret code.

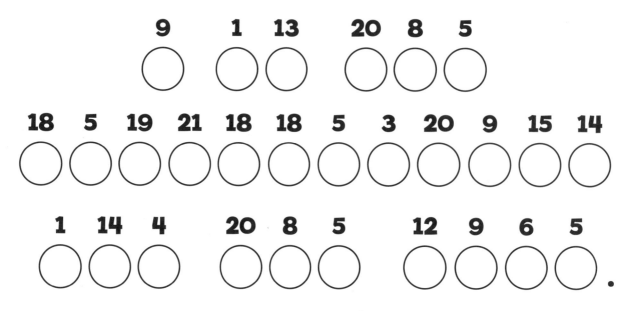

9   1   13   20   8   5

18   5   19   21   18   18   5   3   20   9   15   14

1   14   4   20   8   5   12   9   6   5 .

John 11:25

Maze

Follow the path to the tomb.

START

FINISH

Saul Meets Jesus

Acts 9:1–19

Saul hated the people who believed in Jesus and were telling others about Him. He got permission from the Israelite leaders to throw these Christians in prison. He even had some of them executed. One day, Saul was on his way to Damascus to arrest the Christians there. A bright light appeared in front of Saul, and he fell to the ground. He heard a voice say, "Saul, Saul, why are you persecuting me? I am Jesus, the one you are persecuting. Now, go to Damascus and you will be told what to do."

When he got up, Saul was blind, so he had to have his companions lead him the rest of the way. Jesus told a man named Ananias to help Saul, so Ananias went and prayed with Saul so he could see again. Saul changed his name to Paul, and he became a missionary, telling everyone he met about Jesus.

Find and Count

How many of each item can you find? Write your answers in the boxes.

Jars and pots ☐   Candles ☐   Windows ☐

Puzzle

Where do the scrambled puzzle shapes go?

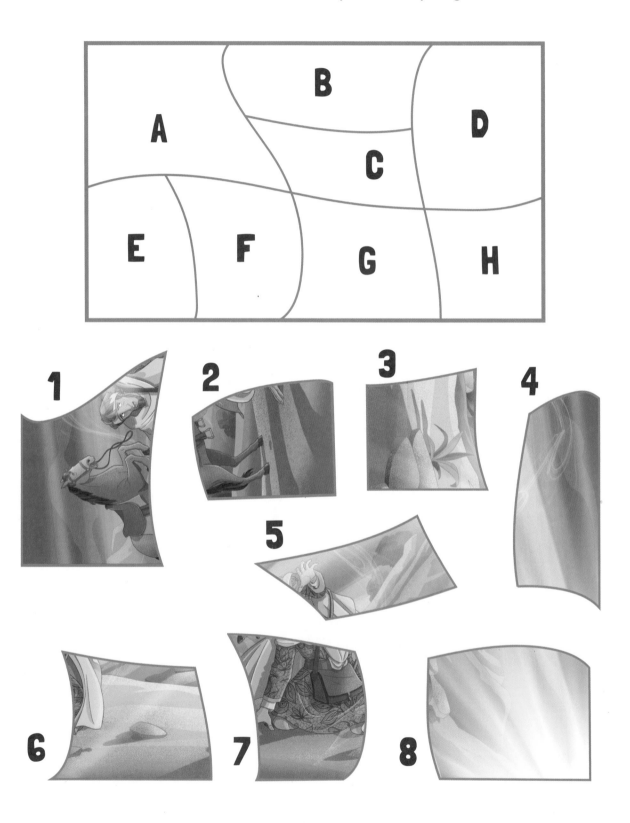

Sequences

Which image is missing from each sequence?

Color the Bible Verse

If we believe that Jesus is truly Christ, we are God's children.

1 John 5:1 (CEV)

Spot the Odd One

Spot the odd one out in each row of pictures.

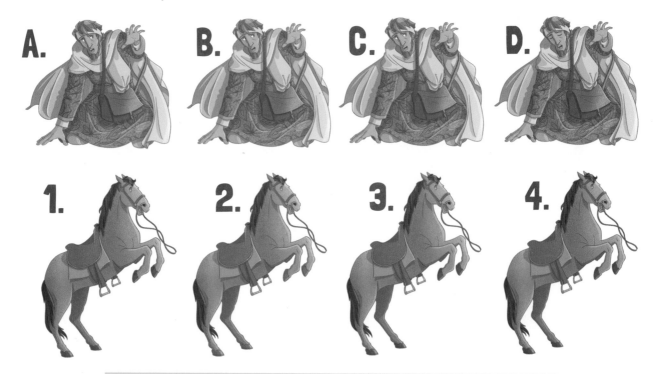

Find the Shadow

Which shadows are the odd ones out?

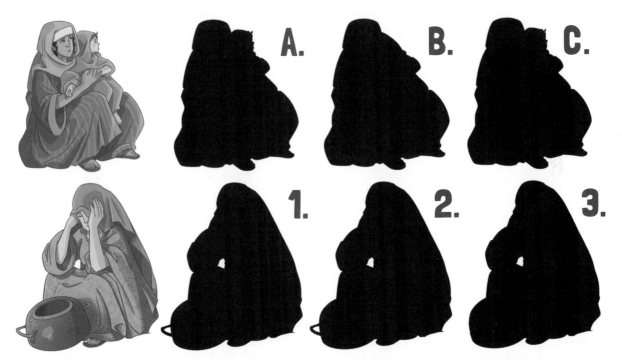

Dot to Dot

Who is in the desert with Paul?

Paul and Silas Praise God in Prison

Acts 16:16–34

Paul and his friend Silas were teaching people about Jesus when some important men in the town they were visiting got mad at them and threw them into prison. Paul and Silas didn't let that stop them from sharing the good news about Jesus, though.

They sang songs and praised God right there in prison so the jailor and all the other prisoners could hear. About midnight, God sent an earthquake that shook the prison and opened all the doors and broke off all the chains. The jailor was afraid that all the prisoners had escaped and that he would be executed for letting them go. "Don't worry," Paul said. "We are all still here!"

The jailor asked Paul, "What do I need to do to be saved?"
"Believe in the Lord Jesus," Paul answered, "and you will be saved."
The jailor and his whole family believed in Jesus that day.

Word Match

Match the words that mean the same thing.

TEACH	**KILL**
EXECUTE	**DESTROY**
BELIEF	**COACH**
BREAK	**FAITH**

Word Search

Find the words in the grid.

A	P	C	O	N	K	E	R	I	D	Y	N	B	X	J	I	G
J	M	T	H	A	S	V	M	W	Z	G	I	P	I	A	Y	Q
H	E	U	F	S	Q	J	U	P	A	U	L	C	K	E	U	E
J	R	J	Y	G	J	Q	A	T	R	H	U	L	W	J	B	E
I	O	W	E	A	L	P	R	I	S	O	N	E	R	Q	N	O
O	I	K	Z	S	G	J	Q	N	L	T	S	Q	S	P	S	H
M	D	M	C	X	U	Y	D	W	Z	O	V	G	I	Y	D	U
C	U	I	V	F	R	S	Z	G	A	M	R	T	L	G	X	M
R	L	T	A	Q	H	P	B	Y	B	Y	J	L	A	R	F	Q
E	O	F	S	I	D	O	A	E	X	K	H	Q	S	V	U	C

Paul

Silas

Jesus

Prisoner

Jailor

Code Breaker

Fill in the Bible verse using the secret code.

A=1
B=2
C=3
D=4
E=5
F=6
G=7
H=8
I=9
J=10
K=11
L=12
M=13
N=14
O=15
P=16
Q=17
R=18
S=19
T=20
U=21
V=22
W=23
X=24
Y=25
Z=26

18 5 10 15 9 3 5   9 14
◯ ◯ ◯ ◯ ◯ ◯ ◯   ◯ ◯

20 8 5   12 15 18 4
◯ ◯ ◯   ◯ ◯ ◯ ◯

1 12 23 1 25 19
◯ ◯ ◯ ◯ ◯ ◯ .

Philippians 4:4

102

Spot the Differences

Can you spot the 8 differences between these 2 pictures?

Sticker Game

Find the sticker shapes on page 114 to complete the picture.

Crossword

Use the story text to help you.

1 Across. A shaking of the ground.

2 Across. A place for locking up criminals.

3 Across. 12 o'clock at night.

1 Down. Expressed admiration.

2 Down. Rescued.

Picture Sudoku

Fill in the sudoku. Which images go where?

A.

B.

C.

D.

Game Solutions

Page 5
9 pink flowers, 10 flying birds, 13 butterflies, 6 horses

Page 7
Crossword
1 Across: beginning, 2 Across: creation, 3 Across: knowledge, 1 Down: animals, 2 Down: Garden

Spot the Odd One
6, B

Page 8
The sea, the sky, the land

Page 12

Page 13

Page 14
Descriptions
Giraffe, panda, elephant

Word Scramble
Giraffe, panda, elephant, crocodile

Page 17
Word Match
Promise = vow, believe = trust, laughter = amusement, joy = happiness

Sequences
1. B, 2. D

Page 21
Family Tree
Sarah, Isaac, Abraham

Word Search

B	T	B	L	E	J	X	C	U	A	J	R	P	S	F	T	A
A	F	V	E	Q	H	O	W	I	S	B	U	Q	D	O	N	U
U	D	L	M	U	K	R	Z	S	N	N	R	L	K	S	M	B
D	W	H	A	O	T	V	E	A	Y	F	P	A	I	A	Q	C
W	F	Z	R	U	E	R	Q	A	V	A	N	M	H	B	J	R
P	N	P	Q	H	G	K	O	C	Y	U	B	C	P	A	N	X
O	E	X	B	P	A	H	C	Y	K	T	D	T	G	L	M	V
I	S	A	R	A	H	J	T	R	V	X	Q	G	I	H	H	O
U	L	T	W	I	F	D	R	E	Y	J	Q	S	O	A	V	T
P	H	C	U	E	L	X	Z	M	R	F	E	L	W	M	R	Z

Page 23
"I hereby put you in charge of the whole land of Egypt."

Page 24
Crossword
1 Across: jealous, 2 Across: dream, 1 Down: eleven, 2 Down: famine, 3 Down: servant

Story Quiz
1. eleven, 2. Egypt, 3. seven, 4. the king

Page 26
4 palm trees, 9 sheep, 2 walking sticks, 11 sandals

Game Solutions

Page 27

B

Page 29

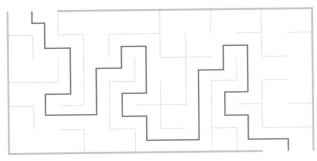

Page 30

Page 31

A. 4, B. 8, C. 2, D. 7, E. 1, F. 6, G. 3, H. 5

Page 32

Page 33

Spot the Odd One

4, C

Word Scramble

Israelites, plague, Egypt, Moses

Page 35

Page 36

Code Breaker

"Your people will be my people and your God my God."

Family Tree

Boaz, Naomi, Ruth

Page 38

B

Page 41

Word Search

N	R	Q	N	Z	M	K	B	W	R	W	E	P	J	A	Q	D
U	Z	E	M	G	A	I	N	D	Z	S	V	C	O	Z	V	O
Q	T	K	U	O	Y	N	J	U	J	E	S	T	H	E	R	H
H	X	V	C	E	R	A	O	X	G	M	X	Y	D	L	T	P
F	P	Y	V	S	A	D	Q	F	H	I	K	P	X	U	B	H
S	K	I	A	O	T	L	E	R	A	J	B	G	E	A	B	M
O	P	E	R	S	I	A	F	C	M	C	U	T	R	S	E	K
X	W	I	X	D	O	T	C	U	A	X	M	F	X	H	C	I
L	J	S	B	D	W	P	G	X	N	I	Z	K	E	C	N	R
H	E	Q	I	Y	L	V	M	F	G	R	W	Y	S	L	E	A

Word Scramble

Mordecai, Xerxes, Persia, Esther

Page 42

Cousin = relative, land = region, chosen = preferred, beauty = allure, king = ruler, woman = female, kingdom = empire, advisor = guide, friend = companion, execute = kill

Game Solutions

Page 43

Sequences
1. B, 2. C

Crossword
1 Across: cousin, 2 Across: uninvited,
1 Down: dinner, 2 Down: beauty

Page 47

18 lions

Page 48

Maze

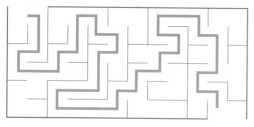

Story Quiz
1. Babylon, 2. three, 3. Darius, 4. Everyone
in the kingdom must pray only to the king.

Page 49

A. 1, B. 4, C. 3, D. 7, E. 8, F. 6, G. 5, H. 2

Page 50

Descriptions
Lions, lion's den, angel

Word Scramble
Babylon, Darius, Daniel, praying

Page 51

Page 53

Line Maze
A

Find the Shadow
C

Page 54

Page 55

Crossword
1 Across: swallow, 2 Across: message,
3 Across: sailor, 1 Down: sinking,
2 Down: whale

Word Search

D	N	H	E	Y	R	A	K	P	B	V	U	C	N	V	T	Q
C	J	N	O	I	N	B	G	V	E	R	O	B	I	A	E	K
H	W	P	T	V	J	W	D	W	H	A	L	E	N	Z	X	W
E	Q	R	G	C	E	A	X	Y	U	M	E	Q	E	A	F	M
E	C	E	D	V	P	R	A	L	E	S	J	T	V	P	C	H
S	I	A	H	F	A	K	B	W	K	Z	N	D	I	D	C	G
M	X	C	P	O	R	B	J	O	P	E	P	R	T	W	G	H
B	L	H	Z	Q	I	Z	M	K	A	O	L	N	E	U	Y	R
V	J	O	N	A	H	B	F	X	W	R	C	U	S	P	L	J
T	S	E	S	Y	O	F	M	J	V	X	D	M	W	I	O	Z

Page 56

1. Nineveh, 2. no, 3. because Jonah
was running away, 4. they threw Jonah
overboard, 5. the storm stopped, 6. three
days, 7. the whale spit him out on the
shore, 8. the Ninevites listened to Jonah's
message and turned to God

Game Solutions

Page 60

Spot the Odd One
4, B

Line Maze
A

Page 62

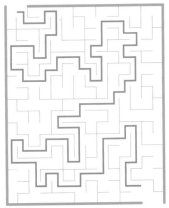

Page 63

Description
1. C, 2. A, 3. B

Word Scramble
Inkeeper, shepherd, worship, savior

Page 65

Page 66

6 baskets, 9 loaves of bread, 9 fish

Page 67

C

Page 68

Word Match
Hungry = ravenous, satisfied = content, miracle = phenomenon, amazed = astounded

Word Scramble
Disciples, fish, loaves, leftovers

Page 71

Code Breaker
"Whoever welcomes this little child in my name welcomes me."

Find the Shadow
4, A

Page 72

Crossword
1 Across: young, 2 Across: disciple, 1 Down: old, 2 Down: big, 3 Down: small

Word Search

D	Q	O	G	Z	S	E	T	Y	K	E	V	E	H	B	P	N
T	J	D	I	S	C	I	P	L	E	S	W	O	R	D	B	F
L	B	S	K	X	H	M	N	V	K	Z	H	L	A	H	J	K
W	N	F	A	Q	I	G	E	P	Q	I	H	M	I	C	U	T
C	O	I	Y	D	L	M	U	A	W	R	N	V	G	Q	Y	A
R	H	B	H	V	D	O	F	R	C	L	O	G	B	P	I	O
F	U	M	R	N	R	T	I	E	F	E	N	I	D	S	X	F
X	H	E	A	V	E	N	X	N	S	P	U	J	A	O	W	L
P	Q	L	O	D	N	M	Q	T	K	S	A	I	M	D	M	X
J	V	Z	B	S	P	Z	G	S	X	H	I	Q	C	Y	E	I

Page 74

A, C, B, D

Game Solutions

Page 77

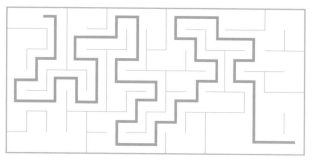

Page 78

Page 79

A. 3, B. 2, C. 6, D. 5, E. 1, F. 8, G. 4, H. 7

Page 81

Crossword

1 Across: cheated, 2 Across: extra,
3 Across: tree, 1 Down: teacher,
2 Down: taxes

Sequences

1. A, 2. C

Page 83

Page 84

Word Match

Leader = ruler, threaten = intimidate, rules
= laws, suffer = endure

Word Scramble

Perfect, trial, painful, Jesus

Page 85

Story Quiz

1. He threatened their power,
2. He never sinned, 3. because Jesus took
our punishment, 4. crucifixion

Word Search

J	W	F	L	Q	D	M	X	B	O	S	S	I	M	C	V	J
R	A	N	W	E	J	V	K	Q	M	E	I	P	N	W	H	A
D	P	O	T	T	N	C	V	R	H	Y	X	N	U	G	J	F
H	V	G	H	L	Y	S	H	P	W	N	V	I	F	R	P	D
U	F	O	R	G	I	V	E	N	E	S	S	O	H	U	T	G
I	T	J	E	B	U	G	Y	O	V	R	U	T	K	Q	L	T
B	M	I	A	L	K	C	R	U	C	I	F	I	X	I	O	N
K	P	N	T	H	N	A	W	J	U	M	F	E	W	M	I	P
R	F	X	E	W	L	G	D	H	B	N	E	P	C	S	A	C
C	Q	M	N	S	E	P	V	F	J	L	R	K	Y	T	X	E

Page 86

33

Page 89

Crossword

1 Across: forever, 2 Across: tomb,
3 Across: angels, 1 Down: perfume,
2 Down: risen

Find the Shadow

E

Game Solutions

Page 92
Word Search

C	I	P	J	E	N	C	O	L	N	M	G	I	O	K	N	A
M	O	K	N	L	A	O	P	D	I	S	C	I	P	L	E	S
K	A	I	R	G	K	F	L	B	I	J	D	L	I	Q	L	H
F	W	G	Z	I	R	L	Q	I	H	R	N	P	M	J	A	J
O	O	G	D	P	E	R	F	U	M	E	N	A	K	L	N	I
B	M	D	G	A	I	O	K	J	P	N	L	N	I	E	Q	O
P	E	O	I	D	L	K	I	Q	D	A	K	G	F	P	B	M
H	N	M	L	J	K	E	L	O	N	G	P	E	J	L	M	C
K	E	J	I	M	B	R	N	R	I	O	R	L	P	C	K	R
A	P	L	F	J	I	H	Q	E	S	J	M	S	J	N	P	E

Code Breaker
"I am the resurrection and the life."

Page 93

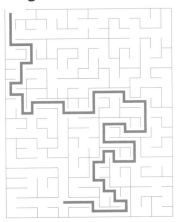

Page 95
6 jars and pots, 3 candles, 2 windows

Page 96
A. 1, B. 4, C. 5, D. 8, E. 2, F. 7, G. 6, H. 3

Page 97
1. B, 2. C

Page 98
Spot the Odd One
D, 2

Find the Shadow
B, 3

Page 101
Word Match
Teach = coach, execute = kill, belief = faith, break = destroy

Word Search

A	P	C	O	N	K	E	R	I	D	Y	N	B	X	J	I	G
J	M	T	H	A	S	V	M	W	Z	G	I	P	I	A	Y	Q
H	E	U	F	S	Q	J	U	P	A	U	L	C	K	E	U	E
J	R	J	Y	G	J	Q	A	T	R	H	U	L	W	J	B	E
I	O	W	E	A	L	P	R	I	S	O	N	E	R	Q	N	O
O	I	K	Z	S	G	J	Q	N	L	T	S	Q	S	P	S	H
M	D	M	C	X	U	Y	D	W	Z	O	V	G	I	Y	D	U
C	U	I	V	F	R	S	Z	G	A	M	R	T	L	G	X	M
R	L	T	A	Q	H	P	B	Y	B	Y	J	L	A	R	F	Q
E	O	F	S	I	D	O	A	E	X	K	H	Q	S	V	U	C

Page 102
"Rejoice in the Lord always."

Page 103

Page 105
Crossword
1 Across: earthquake, 2 Across: prison, 3 Across: midnight, 1 Down: praised, 2 Down: saved

Picture Sudoku

(pot)	(person)	(bowl)	(candle)
(candle)	B	D	C
C	D	A	(bowl)
(bowl)	A	(person)	D

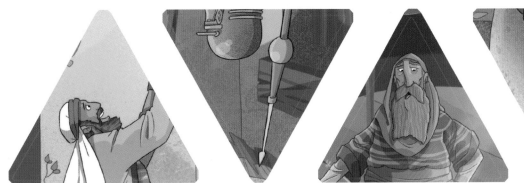